Nia's Big Day

By **Koya Bell**

illustrated by
Creativepony

Nia's Big Day

By **Koya Bell**

illustrated by
Creativepony

Dedicated to my sweet
baby girl Nehemiah

"Good Morning Nia!" Mommie said,
"Are you excited about your big day?"

"Good Morning Mommie! Yes I am".
Nia replied, with a big smile on her face.

"Okay Nia, It's time to get ready for your first day of school." Mommie explained.

"Okay Mommie!
Time to brush my teeth!"
Nia shouted.

After Nia's bath Mommie asked,
"What would you like to wear?"

"Hmmm! Let me see." Nia said
"How about this one?" Nia replied,
holding up her favorite unicorn dress.

Nia was all dressed and ready to go.
"How about some breakfast? I made your favorite." Mommie told her.
"Yay! Oatmeal!" Nia shouted with excitement.
"Yummy Yummy."

"All done mommie!" Nia said. "Good job baby." Mommie replied. "Now it's time to head out and catch your school bus."

Nia was so excited to ride the school bus. "Okay Mommie, I'm ready! Let's go! Bye-bye Daddy!" Nia said, as she ran and gave him a great big hug. "Have a good first day Nia." Daddy told her smiling.

As mommie and Nia were walking down the sidewalk, they could see the school bus approaching. "The bus is coming! The bus is coming!" Nia shouted repeatedly.

BUS STOP

"Alright come on up," the bus
driver instructed.
"Hi! I'm Nia and it's
my first day of school,"
"Oh how exciting!"
the bus driver replied.

Nia turned to wave bye to her mommie
as she walked to her seat.

As the bus drove away mommie stood there waving.
"Bye bye Nia have a great first day of school."

Made in the USA
Middletown, DE
30 July 2021